SONIC ™
THE HEDGEHOG

ZETI HUNT!

SEGA ®

IDW

@IDWpublishing
IDWpublishing.com

Cover Art by
Abby Bulmer

Cover Colors by
Joana Lafuente

Series Assistant Edits by
Riley Farmer

Series Edits by
David Mariotte

Collection Edits by
Alonzo Simon
and **Zac Boone**

Collection Design by
Shawn Lee

ISBN: 978-1-68405-975-1

25 24 23 22   1 2 3 4

Originally published as
SONIC THE HEDGEHOG issues #41–44.

Nachie Marsham, Publisher
Blake Kobashigawa, SVP Sales, Marketing & Strategy
Tara McCrillis, VP Publishing Operations
Anna Morrow, VP Marketing & Publicity
Alex Hargett, VP Sales
Scott Dunbier, Director, Special Projects
Greg Gustin, Sr. Director, Content Strategy
Lauren LePera, Managing Editor
Joe Hughes, Director, Talent Relations
Keith Davidsen, Director, Marketing & PR
Topher Alford, Sr. Digital Marketing Manager
Patrick O'Connell, Sr. Manager, Direct Market Sales
Shauna Monteforte, Sr. Director of Manufacturing Operations
Greg Foreman, Director DTC Sales & Operations
Nathan Widick, Sr. Art Director, Head of Design
Neil Uyetake, Sr. Art Director, Design & Production
Shawn Lee, Art Director, Design & Production
Jack Rivera, Art Director, Marketing

Ted Adams and Robbie Robbins, IDW Founders

SEGA®

Special thanks to Mai Kiyotaki, Michael Cisneros, Sandra Jo, Sonic Team,
and everyone at Sega for their invaluable assistance.

STORY **IAN FLYNN**

ART **ADAM BRYCE THOMAS** (#41)
TRACY YARDLEY (#42 & 44)
JAMAL PEPPERS (#43)
BRACARDI CURRY (#43)
THOMAS ROTHLISBERGER (#43)
ADDITIONAL INKS **MATT FROESE** (#42 & 44)
REGGIE GRAHAM (#43)
COLORS **MATT HERMS** (#41-42 & 44)
REGGIE GRAHAM (#43)
VALENTINA PINTO (#43)
LETTERS **SHAWN LEE**
NATHAN WIDICK (#43)

ART BY **ADAM BRYCE THOMAS**

ORCHARDVILLE.

THUD

THERE'S MORE OF THOSE THINGS?!

THAT RUNTY ONE WAS BAD ENOUGH!

PATHETIC. THIS TOWN FELL SO EASILY. I DO HOPE THE OTHERS PUT UP SOME FIGHT.

I'LL DISTRACT HIM. YOU HAVE TO SEND WORD TO THE OTHERS.

ART BY **NATALIE HAINES**

ART BY **PRISCILLA TRAMONTANO**

THANK YOU FOR ALL RESPONDING SO QUICKLY. ALLOW ME TO BRING EVERYONE UP TO SPEED.

THE CHAOTIX HAVE ASSEMBLED IN SUNSET CITY.

HI, JEWEL!

TAILS JOINS US FROM HIS WORKSHOP IN CENTRAL CITY.

AND SONIC IS IN WINTERBURG, WHICH HE REACHED IN RECORD TIME.

IT'S WHAT I DO.

I KNEW WE'D HAVE TO DEAL WITH THE DEADLY SIX EVENTUALLY, SO I'VE BEEN WORKSHOPPING SOME OPTIONS.

I PRESENT TO YOU--THE *ZETI ZAPPER!*

I BUILT THEM BY REVERSE-ENGINEERING ZAVOK'S CHAOS EMERALD SIPHON.

THEY'LL TURN THEIR OWN ELECTRO-MAGNETIC POWERS AGAINST THEM, HARMLESSLY DISABLING THEM FOR CAPTURE AND TRANSPORT...

...ABOARD THE ZETI LAUNCHER!

IT WILL AUTOMATICALLY RETURN THEM TO LOST HEX WHERE THEY WON'T BE ABLE TO BOTHER ANYONE!

WHAT IF THEY REMOVE THE ZAPPERS MID-FLIGHT? COULDN'T THEY TAKE CONTROL OF THE ROCKET?

I'VE BUILT SAFE-GUARDS AGAINST ALL THAT. THE HARDEST PART WILL BE TAKING THEM DOWN.

*STH#37-40--EDS.

MY *TRICORE* WOULD BE POWERFUL ENOUGH TO STORM THE FACILITY, BUT THAT'S DR. EGGMAN'S STYLE. NOT MINE. I'M TRYING TO BE BETTER.

AND MY HYPNOTIC TOOLS ONLY GOT ME INTO THE PRISON BECAUSE I WASN'T KNOWN TO SECURITY.*

I SHOULD ASSUME I'D BE IDENTIFIED ON SIGHT HERE.

*STH "BAD GUYS" #1--EDS.

NO, I NEED TO MINIMIZE MY CONTACTS. I'VE SEEN PEOPLE ENTER THIS SHED, BUT NEVER LEAVE. PERHAPS THERE'S A TRAP DOOR OR...

EUREKA! BUT THERE'S NO TIME TO CELEBRATE. I MUST BE EXCEEDINGLY CAUTIOUS.

I DIDN'T HAVE THE LUXURY OF ESTABLISHING ANY KIND OF DISTRACTION...

WHAM

ART BY **MATT HERMS**

DR. EGGMAN LOST HIS MEMORIES AFTER ONE OF HIS MOST CRITICAL DEFEATS.

HE TOOK ON THE PERSONA OF *MR. TINKER*, A KINDLY INVENTOR AND REPAIR MAN.

SO I TOOK HIM IN AND WENT TO GREAT LENGTHS TO CURE HIM OF THAT STATE OF MIND.

WITH... SOME ASSISTANCE FROM METAL SONIC...

"THEN ONE DAY... HE VANISHED.

"NOT LONG AFTER, EGGMAN ATTACKED.

"THE METAL VIRUS DIDN'T AFFECT ME...

"...AND I WAS *VERY* ALONE."

TO BE CONTINUED!

ART BY **JAMAL PEPPERS**

ART BY **NATHALIE FOURDRAINE**

ART BY **NATHALIE FOURDRAINE**

ART BY **NATHALIE FOURDRAINE**

SONIC™ THE HEDGEHOG

ZETI HUNT!